# Travel to Egypt
## with
# Joseph

## AN ACTION RHYME BOOK

# Travel to Egypt
## with
# Joseph

Marjory Francis and Chris Saunderson

Hold out arms and turn around

Look, look!

Show the coat to your brothers.
Look at the colours with Joseph.

Tumble, tumble!
Fall into the pit.
Fall down and down with Joseph.

Roll hands

**Trudge, trudge.**
Walk along slowly.
Follow the camels with Joseph.

Walk slowly on the spot

Sweep the floor

**Sweep, sweep.**
Work in the house.
Work very hard with Joseph.

Clunk, clunk.
Hear the key turning,
Down in the prison with Joseph.

Hand behind ear

**Bow, bow.**
Bow to the king.
Bow to King Pharaoh with Joseph.

Bow down

Dress, dress.
Wear the fine clothing.
Put on the King's ring with Joseph.

Put ring on finger

**Build, build.**
Build the walls higher.
Build the big storehouse with Joseph.

Build with fists

Watch, watch!
Here come the brothers.
Watch them arrive with Joseph.

Two hands over brow

**Smile, smile.**
Smile, but don't show it.
His brothers don't know it is Joseph.

Smile behind hand

**Oh! Oh!**
What a surprise!
The brothers have found that it's Joseph.

Mouth open, hand over mouth

Happy hug

**Hug, hug.**
Here's Joseph's father.
Welcome the family with Joseph.

Published in the UK by Scripture Union

207-209 Queensway, Bletchley, Milton Keynes, Bucks, MK2 2EB

ISBN 978 1 84427 257 0


First edition 2007

Editorial Director Annette Reynolds

Editor Nicola Bull

Art Director Gerald Rogers

Pre-production Krystyna Kowalska Hewitt

Production John Laister